Steve
varic   nd a
puppeteer in England, and in Botswana, Africa. He met Steve
Skidmore at a school in Nottingham and the Two Steves began
writing together Steve Barlow   d sails
a boat named *Which Way*, so   ually hasn't
                  a clue wh   ng.

Steve S   u less hairier than Steve Barlow.
       After passing   exams at school, he went on to
Nottingham University where he spent most of his time
playing sport and doing a variety of heroic summer jobs,
including counting pastry pie lids (honest). He trained as a
teacher of Drama, English and Film studies, before teaming
up with Steve Barlow to become a full-time author.

Together they have written many books, including:
The Mad Myths series
Find out more at:
www.the2steves.net

ABOUT THE ILLUSTRATOR

Sonia Leong is based in Cambridge, in the UK, and is a
superstar manga artist. She won Tokyopop's first UK Rising
Stars of Manga competition (2005-06) and her first graphic
novel was *Manga Shakespeare: Romeo and Juliet*. She's a
member of Sweatdrop Studios and has too many awards
to fit in this teeny space.

Find Sonia at her website: **www.fyredrake.net**

I HERO

Save the Empire!

Steve Barlow and Steve Skidmore
Illustrated by Sonia Leong

W
FRANKLIN WATTS
LONDON•SYDNEY

First published in 2008
by Franklin Watts

Text © Steve Barlow and Steve Skidmore 2008
Illustrations © Sonia Leong 2008

A CIP catalogue record for this book
is available from the British Library.

ISBN: 978 0 7496 8265 1

1 3 5 7 9 10 8 6 4 2

Printed in Great Britain

Franklin Watts is a division of Hachette Children's Books,
an Hachette Livre UK company.
www.hachettelivre.co.uk

Decide your own destiny...

This book is not like others you may have read. *You* are the hero of this adventure. It is up to you to make decisions that will affect how the adventure unfolds.

Each section of this book is numbered. At the end of most sections, you will have to make a choice. The choice you make will take you to a different section of the book.

Some of your choices will help you to complete the adventure successfully. But choose carefully, some of your decisions could be fatal!

If you fail, then start the adventure again and learn from your mistake.

If you choose correctly you will succeed in your adventure.

Don't be a zero, be a hero!

It is September 1851. You are a famous private detective living in London. Whenever the police at Scotland Yard are unable to solve a crime, they always call on you to help them.

Queen Victoria is on the throne and the British Empire is the greatest in the world. However, it is a time of great tension between Britain and Russia. The Russians are trying to expand their empire in the Middle East and Afghanistan in an attempt to drive out Britain from India.

It is also the year of the Great Exhibition. This is designed to display the industrial power of Britain. It is being held in the newly built Crystal Palace in Hyde Park, and has been visited by thousands of people from around the world.

It is almost midnight and you are reading a copy of the *Illustrated London News* in your rooms, when you hear a knock at the door. Your housekeeper enters and informs you that two gentlemen are at the front door. They wish to see you urgently.

You wonder who would be calling at this time of night, and tell her to let them in.

Now turn to section 1.

1

Before the door opens, you know that one of the men is Inspector Bowles of Scotland Yard – you can smell his terrible cologne! You have worked with him on many cases in the past. The door opens to reveal the Inspector and another person, who looks vaguely familiar.

You greet Bowles. "Hello, Inspector. What brings you out at this time of night, and who is your companion?"

"This is Mr Brown," replies Bowles. "He is working with me on a matter of national security."

You raise an eyebrow. You are sure that you have seen a picture of 'Mr Brown' recently.

If you think you know who Mr Brown is, go to 28.

If you don't know, go to 14.

2

You climb into the carriage and realise that there is somebody else inside.

Before you can react, you are held fast and a piece of cloth is thrust over your mouth and nose. The cloth is soaked in chloroform. You try to hold your breath, but it is useless. You breathe in the knock-out drug and pass out.

Go to 48.

3

The Inspector hurries off as you move to the side gallery keeping a close watch on the entrance.

Minutes pass. Just as you think this is a waste of time, you see two men approaching. They are joined by a man with a black beard. They shake hands and move towards the entrance to the diamond exhibition. You must make a decision quickly.

If you decide to shoot the bearded man, go to 12.

If you want to rush out and challenge the men, go to 30.

If you decide just to follow them, go to 24.

4

You pretend to feel ill, and stagger into the table.

"Sorry gentlemen, I'm just an old sea dog," you say.

"Get him out of here!" shouts the bearded man as he leaps up. He has a familiar voice. The other men step forward and you seize your chance. You knock one down and shoot the other before the bearded man sprints off in surprise. You chase him out the door towards the docks.

Go to 15.

5

"This is a simple code," you say.

You hold the paper up to a mirror and read the message:

KOH-I-NOR DIAMOND
BLACK BEARD
RUSSIAN
MIDDAY FRIDAY 19TH

"That is tomorrow!" you exclaim. "The Koh-i-nor diamond is one of the exhibits at the Great Exhibition in Hyde Park. It is obvious that there is to be a meeting between the Russians and the Brotherhood. It is a good place to meet, with so many people around. I suggest that we are also there!"

You wish the Inspector and Sir Archibald goodnight and retire to your bed, wondering what tomorrow will bring.

Go to 23.

6

You edge closer to the bearded man – he smells very familar. But can you remember which pocket he placed the paper in?

If you choose to pick his left-hand coat pocket, go to 21.

If you choose to pick his right-hand coat pocket, go to 46.

If you decide not to pick his pocket after all but continue to follow him, go to 16.

7

You race after the cab, but you are not fast enough – the carriage is getting away.

Just as you are about to give up the chase, a horse and wagon blocks the road ahead and the cab is forced to stop.

Within seconds you have reached the carriage. But what should you do?

If you decide to shoot the driver, go to 17.

If you wish to climb inside the carriage, go to 2.

If you want to jump on top of the carriage, go to 31.

8

"Hide? No, I will stay here," you tell the Inspector. "To try and lure these conspirators into the open." The Inspector nods and hurries off to the main entrance.

You look around for any suspicious characters, but there is no one that catches your eye. The minutes pass. You glance at your watch — it is now well past midday. You have to decide whether to stay where you are or move to a hiding place.

If you move to the side gallery, go to 3.

If you move to the upper gallery, go to 47.

If you decide to stay where you are, go to 30.

9

"You have lied to me, gentlemen," you say. "Please leave at once."

Despite their protests, you show them to the door and return to your reading.

You will never know why they needed your help. Your pride has stopped any chance you had of being a hero.

If you wish to start the adventure again, go back to 1.

10

You pull out the paper you took from the cab driver and compare it with the new piece of paper.

```
A 1    F 6    K 11   P 16   U 21
B 2    G 7    L 12   Q 17   V 22
C 3    H 8    M 13   R 18   W 23
D 4    I 9    N 14   S 19   X 24
E 5    J 10   O 15   T 20   Y 25
                            Z 26
```

13,5,5,20   13,9,4,14,9,7,8,20

19,8,9,16   9,14,14   12,9,13,5,8,15,21,19,5

If you wish to go to Limehouse at midnight, go to 43.

If you wish to go to the Tower of London immediately, go to 41.

11

You give chase, but the bearded man is too fast. Before long you have lost him. You stop and look around desperately. Out of the corner of your eye, you think you see him disappearing into a dark alleyway, but cannot be sure.

If you wish go down the alleyway, go to 20.

If you decide to return to the driver and search for clues, go to 27.

12

You take out your revolver, aim and pull the trigger. There is a crack and the bearded man falls to the floor.

Screams and shouts fill the hall as people run for the exits.

Amidst the chaos and confusion you make your way to the fallen man. As you bend over the man, a policeman charges at you waving his loud police rattle and strikes you with a wooden truncheon. You slump to the ground, unconscious.

Go to 18.

13

You are an expert at disguises and you spend the next hour disguising yourself as an old sailor. You look in the mirror and are happy that no one will recognise you.

Go to 33.

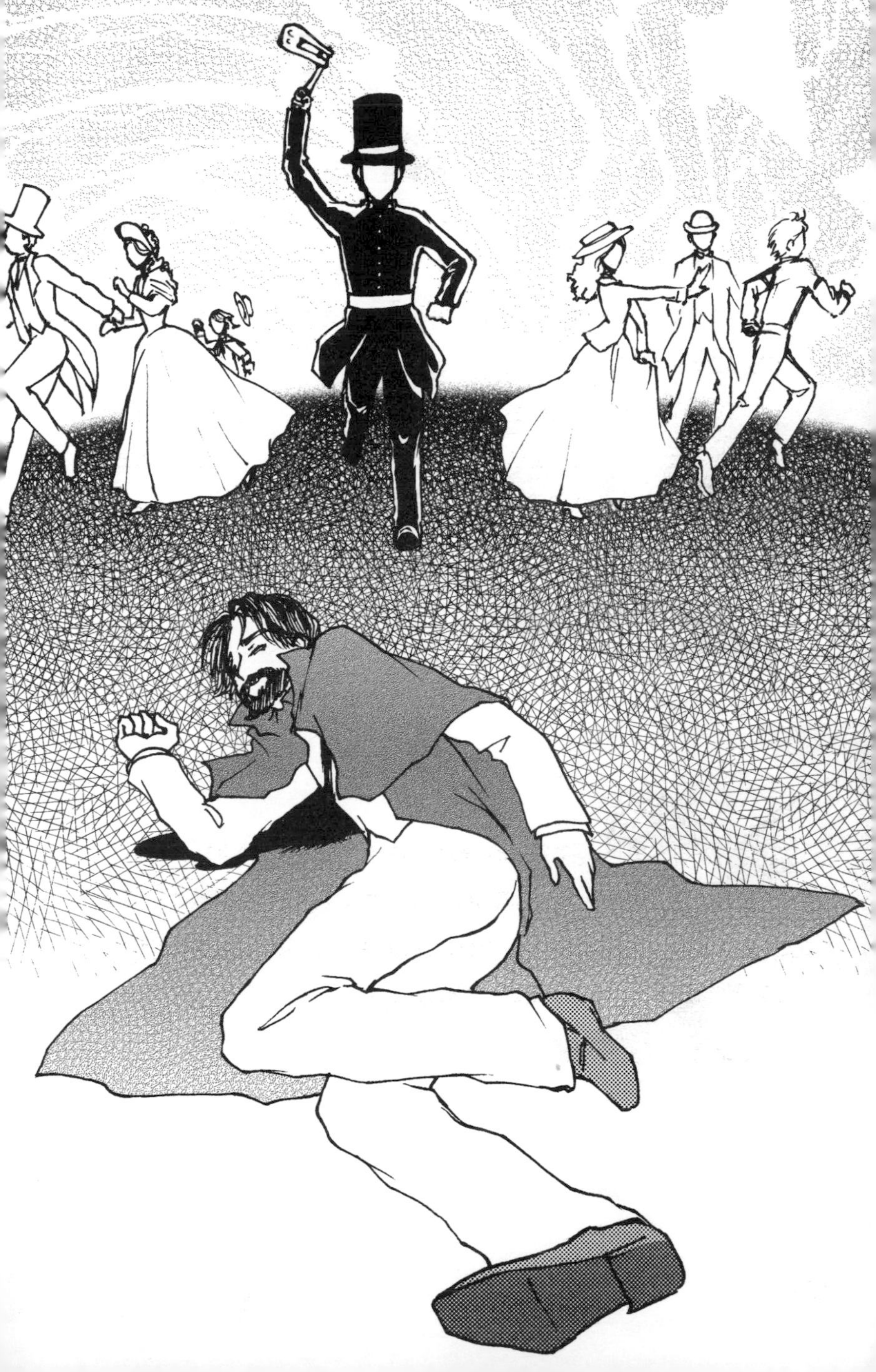

14

As you sit back down in your seat, you glance at the paper you were reading and gasp. There is a picture of Mr Brown on the front page! But the name under the picture is different! You realise that Inspector Bowles is lying.

If you are offended at being lied to, go to 9.

If you wish to confront 'Mr Brown' with your discovery, go to 28.

15

You race towards the docks and catch sight of the bearded man heading into a riverside warehouse. You hurry to the warehouse and step inside.

The only light comes from an oil lamp. There is no sign of the bearded man, but ahead of you is a doorway. To the right there are bales of cotton and several large crates. What should you do?

If you wish to go through the doorway, go to 20.

If you wish to check out the crates, go to 22.

16

The man heads into Hyde Park and you follow from a distance. He makes his way towards the Serpentine Lake.

Suddenly he turns and faces you, a revolver in his hand. "Did you really think that I didn't know you were following me?"

Before you can move a shot rings out and you feel a searing pain. You look down and see blood spurting from your chest. It is your last sight as you drop to the floor.

You have paid the ultimate price. If you wish to start your adventure again, go to 1.

17

You take aim at the driver and pull the trigger. He falls from the cab onto the cobbled street.

You rush over to the man and kneel over him. A pool of blood spreads onto the road. With his last breath the driver points at the carriage and whispers, "Inside…"

If you wish to search inside the cab, go to 2.
If you wish to search the man's pockets for clues, go to 37.

18

You wake up in a police cell.

Inspector Bowles enters. He is angry. "Why on earth did you shoot an innocent member of the public without finding out who he was?"

"He looked suspicious," you reply sheepishly. "I thought he was part of the Brotherhood of the Black Widow."

The Inspector stares at you. "Thanks to your lack of thinking, we have lost all our leads. Sir Archibald is furious – you have let down your country."

Your adventure has ended. If you wish to begin again, go to 1.

19

Before Archibald can react, you throw the oil lamp at the cotton. The bales burst into flames and the fire quickly spreads.

With a cry of anger, Archibald shoots at you, but you dive out of the way. Soon the fire will reach the crates. You rush towards the door. Archibald shoots at you through the flames.

As you reach the door there is a huge explosion. The force of the blast throws you out of the warehouse onto the cobbles of the dock side. Through dazed eyes, you see the warehouse engulfed in flames. Then you pass out.

Go to 50.

20

You step forward and peer into the darkness. You can see nothing so you inch your way along, revolver at the ready.

Suddenly there is a sound behind you. You spin around, but before you can fire a shot, you are struck on the head and you fall senseless to the ground.

Go to 48.

21

The man turns towards you.

There is a flash of steel and you feel a sharp pain in your side. The man moves away. You can make out the shape of a dagger in his hand. You look down and see blood pouring from a wound. You clutch at your side and try to cry out as you fall to the floor, but it is hopeless.

Your adventure has ended. If you wish to begin again, go to 1.

22

You take the oil lamp over to the crates. By its flickering light you read the writing stencilled on the crate: HALE & CO.

You have found the rockets! But before you can open the crates, the bearded man steps out of the shadows. He has a revolver and it is aimed at you.

"So near but so far," he says. "Drop your gun."

You obey and ask, "Who are you?"

"A member of the Brotherhood." He reaches up and pulls at his beard. It is false. You gasp as you realise who is standing before you.

"Sir Archibald! You traitor! Why?"

"I want to be on the winning side – unlike you. And besides, the Russians are going to pay me well for these rockets… But first I need to be rid of your meddling."

How will you get out of this situation?

If you want to attack Sir Archibald, go to 30.

If you decide to throw the oil lamp at the cotton bales, go to 19.

23

Next morning, you step out of your house. There is a carriage waiting across the road.

"Need a lift, guv'nor?" asks the driver.

"Yes, take me to the Great Exhibition at Hyde Park," you reply.

As you step towards the carriage, there is a gust of wind which lifts the driver's shirt cuff to reveal his forearm. You see a tattoo of a black spider. The driver quickly covers it up.

If you wish to get into the carriage, go to 2.

If you are suspicious about the driver, go to 40.

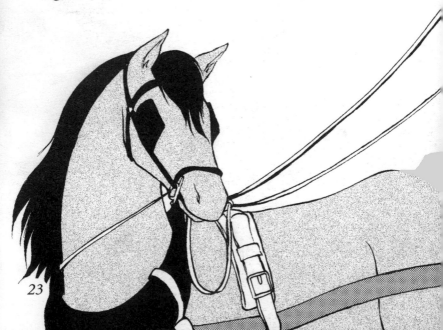

24

Carefully, you follow the suspects through the entrance to the Koh-i-nor exhibition. The three men make their way through the crowds to the cage where the diamond is displayed. You push forward to get close enough to hear their whispered conversation.

"Like the Koh-i-nor diamond was removed from India, so the British will be removed once we have the rockets," says one of the men in a Russian accent.

The bearded man nods. "Where shall I deliver them?" he asks.

You see a piece of paper being handed over. The bearded man looks at it before putting it into his right-hand coat pocket.

"Until tomorrow," he says and disappears into the crowd.

If you want to try to follow the bearded man, go to 42.

If you wish to follow the two men, go to 34.

If you wish to attempt to arrest all three men, go to 30.

25

Holding your revolver, you move slowly into the trees.

You see one of the men standing a few feet away.

"Put up your hands!" you order.

He obeys, but you have been tricked. You hear a noise behind you. You turn but it is too late. The second man crashes the butt of his gun onto your head and you pass out.

Go to 48.

26

The talking inside the inn stops as people stare at you suspiciously.

At the bar you see the bearded man. What should you do now?

If you decide to attack him, go to 21.

If you decide to find a seat and keep an eye on him, go to 30.

27

You search through the dead man's pockets and pull out a piece of paper. You read it.

A 1	F 6	K 11	P 16	U 21
B 2	G 7	L 12	Q 17	V 22
C 3	H 8	M 13	R 18	W 23
D 4	I 9	N 14	S 19	X 24
E 5	J 10	O 15	T 20	Y 25
				Z 26

You wonder what it means.

You search inside the carriage, but there are no more clues to be found. You decide to head for the Great Exhibition.

Turn to 35.

28

You shake your head. "I do not like to be lied to, Mr Brown, or should I say, Sir Archibald Rodgers of the Foreign Office. Your picture is in the *Illustrated London News*."

Inspector Bowles and Sir Archibald look embarrassed.

"I am sorry we tried to deceive you," says Sir Archibald. "I didn't wish to alarm you as the country is in great danger and only you can help. Please accept my apologies."

If you wish to accept the apology, go to 44.
If you are offended at being lied to, go to 9.

29

You pull out your revolver. "I am here to save the Empire! Surrender!"

One of the men leaps at you. You pull your trigger and he drops down dead. The second man also attacks and you deal with him in the same way.

However, in the confusion the bearded man rushes out of the back door. You follow him outside into the darkness and look left and right. One way leads towards the docks, the other leads into an alley.

If you want to go down the alley, go to 20.

If you decide to head towards the docks, go to 15.

30

Before you can move, a strange-looking man steps in front of you. He is holding a thin pipe to his lips. You realise that it is a blowpipe and it is pointing at you!

Before you can say anything you feel a sharp pain in your neck. You reach up and pull out a small dart.

Numbness spreads quickly from your neck through your body. Too late, you realise that you have been poisoned, and you fall to the floor.

Your adventure has ended. If you wish to begin again, turn back to 1.

31

You clamber up onto the carriage. The driver turns around and flails at you with his whip.

You fight back, but he catches you with a blow to the head and you fall towards the ground. In desperation you grab at the door handle and hold on as the cab hurtles along the road.

Hanging on, you reach into your pocket and take out your revolver. However, as you take aim at the driver, the carriage door flaps open.

If you wish to climb inside, go to 2.
If you decide to shoot at the driver, go to 17.

32

"Tell me more about the Brotherhood of the Black Widow," you say.

Sir Archibald frowns. "It is a group sworn to overthrowing the British Empire. Members of the Brotherhood give help to the enemies of Britain. We believe that they were involved in the Afghan and Chinese Opium wars in the 1840s."

"Then they weren't very successful," you say. "The Empire won those conflicts."

"Nevertheless," continues Sir Archibald, "they created problems for us."

You still wish to know more. "How many members belong to this society?"

Sir Archibald shakes his head. "We don't have that information. There could be dozens. However, we do know that the members of the Brotherhood have a distinguishing mark – a tattoo of a black widow spider on their left forearms."

"And why do you think the Brotherhood is behind the robbery?" you ask.

To find out, turn to 39.

33

You take a cab across the city but get out and walk the final mile towards the Ship Inn.

It is a foggy night and you can hardly see the ground in front of you. Finally you reach the inn. You push open the door and enter the gloomy, smoky room. It is full of sailors and workers from all corners of the globe.

If you are in disguise, go to 45.

If you are not, go to 26.

34

You follow the two men from a safe distance. They leave the Crystal Palace and make their way through Hyde Park, heading in the direction of Buckingham Palace.

Suddenly they break into a run. They knew that they were being followed! You give chase, but they lose you amongst the trees.

If you follow them into the woods, go to 25.

If you decide to go back to look for the bearded man, go to 42.

35

You arrive at Hyde Park and make your way into the Crystal Palace.

The iron and glass building is enormous and there are crowds of people who are viewing the many exhibits.

Finally you reach the entrance to the pavilion where the Koh-i-Nor diamond is being displayed. Inspector Bowles is also there, waiting for you.

"I am glad that you survived the attack on your life," he says.

"How did you know about that?" you ask.

"A constable found the dead cab driver," replies the Inspector. "He was a member of the Brotherhood." The Inspector looks at his watch. "It is nearly midday. I will go to the main entrance of the palace. You stay here and hide." You glance around, looking for a place to conceal yourself. There are two galleries – one to the side of the entrance to the exhibition and another one above you, where you can look down.

If you wish to hide in the side gallery, go to 3.

If you wish to climb the stairs to the gallery above you, go to 47.

If you don't want to hide, go to 8.

36

You look at the paper. It is covered in numbers.

13,5,5,20   13,9,4,14,9,7,8,20

19,8,9,16   9,14,14   12,9,13,5,8,15,21,19,5

If you think you know how to crack the code, go to 10.

If you want to challenge the bearded man about the code, go to 16.

37

As you reach towards the dead man's pocket, you hear the cab door opening. You spin round to see a man with a black beard, running away. You shoot at him, but this time your aim is not true and you miss.

If you wish to chase after the bearded man, go to 11.

If you want to continue searching the dead man, go to 27.

38

You wait a couple of minutes before following the bearded man into the back room. You enter and see him sitting at a table with the two men you saw at the Great Exhibition.

They look up. "Who are you?" says one of the men.

If you wish to try and bluff your way out of the situation, go to 4.

If you decide to attack them, go to 29.

If you choose to leave the room, go to 21.

39

Sir Archibald continues. "As you are no doubt aware, Russia is growing in power. We believe that the Russians wish to drive us British out of India. Russian agents have been in contact with the Brotherhood to help them achieve this aim. We believe the Brotherhood is going to supply the Russians with these new rockets. If they do, the British Empire could fall…"

"How do you know this?"

Inspector Bowles replies, "Scotland Yard had an informer in the Brotherhood."

You raise an eyebrow. "Had?"

Inspector Bowles nods. "He was found floating in the Thames earlier this evening with a knife in his back. We found this in his pocket." The Inspector hands you a smudged piece of paper.

If you think you can read the message, go to 5.

If you cannot understand the message, go to 49.

40

As you step towards the carriage, you reach into your coat and pull out your revolver. You point it towards the driver.

"Do not move. You are a member of the Brotherhood of the Black Widow. Your tattoo has given you away. Who ordered you to pick me up?"

Before you can get an answer, the driver whips his horse and the carriage hurtles off.

If you wish to shoot at the driver, go to 17.

If you want to run after the cab, go to 7.

41

You head out of the Exhibition. A carriage pulls up.

"Take me to the Tower of London," you tell the driver.

Go to 2.

42

You look for the bearded man in the crowd. Just when you think you've completely lost him, you spot him caught in a crowd of people leaving the Exhibition. You close in, making sure that he does not see you.

Here is an opportunity to get close to him!

If you wish to try and pick his pocket for the piece of paper, go to 6.

If you decide just to carry on following him, go to 16.

43

You return to your rooms, where you check over the message again.

Meet midnight Ship Inn Limehouse

Limehouse is in the East End of the city next to the River Thames. It is a dangerous place.

If you wish to go in disguise, go to 13.

If you aren't afraid and don't wish to disguise yourself, go to 33.

44

"Very well," you say, "but let that be an end to the lies. Now tell me what brings you to my door."

The Inspector begins, "You have heard of William Hale?"

You nod. "The inventor of the 24-pound Hale rocket – the first iron rocket to spin like a bullet from a gun. This makes it more accurate and deadly than the Congreve rocket, presently used by our army and navy. I believe that Mr Hale has been selling the rocket's design to several foreign governments. The Americans used it in the recent Mexican war."

Sir Archibald is impressed. "You are well informed," he says.

"You have to be in my line of work," you reply. "It can be the difference between life and death."

Sir Archibald continues. "Mr Hale has been working on a new rocket. It is more accurate and contains more explosive. It is a deadly weapon. However, two nights ago there was a robbery at his factory. Two crates of these new rockets were stolen. We believe that members of a secret society called the Brotherhood of the Black Widow took them."

If you wish to know more about this society, go to 32.

If you wish to know more about the robbery, go to 39.

45

No one takes any notice of you as you make your way to the bar and order a drink. You take it to a seat, where you can observe what is going on.

Just before midnight the door opens and the bearded man enters. The landlord greets him and nods towards a back room. The bearded man heads towards the room.

If you decide to follow him, go to 38.
If you decide to attack him, go to 21.

46

You move to the man and 'accidentally' bump into him. You dip your hand into his pocket and pull out the paper.

If you wish to move away and read what is written on the paper, go to 36.

If you wish to continue to follow the man, go to 16.

If you wish to try and pick his other pocket for further clues, go to 21.

47

The Inspector hurries off and you head up the stairs to the gallery overlooking the entrance.

After some minutes you notice a man with a black beard pushing his way through the crowd. Two other men move forward and greet the man. They head towards the entrance to the diamond exhibition. What should you do?

If you decide to shoot the bearded man, go to 12.

If you decide to follow the group, go to 24.

48

You wake up to find that your hands and feet are tightly bound. It is dark, but you can make out the shape of several large wooden crates. The sound of water outside makes you realise that you are in the hold of a moving ship.

A door opens and a black-bearded man carrying a lantern enters.

"Who are you?" you ask.

He draws back his sleeve to reveal the tattoo of a black widow spider on his forearm. "I am a member of the Brotherhood. But you'll never know my true identity. Russia is where we're delivering these rockets. But on the way, we're going to drop off something." He smiles. "You – into the sea."

There is no escape. Your adventure has ended. If you wish to begin again, turn back to 1.

49

"This message makes no sense," you say.

Sir Archibald turns to Inspector Bowles and frowns. "You said this man was supposed to be the best private detective in London. We have made a mistake. You are obviously not the man to help save the Empire. Come, Inspector, we need to find someone who is up to the task."

They both leave.

You have failed. If you wish to begin your adventure again, go back to 1.

50

A week later you are resting in your rooms. The front doorbell rings and moments later your housekeeper shows in Inspector Bowles.

"I am glad to see you have recovered," he says. "A messy business. Who would have thought Sir Archibald would be a traitor? Why do you think he did what he did?"

"Perhaps it was the money – or that he thought he would be a hero. Now he is dead though, the Brotherhood's plan is in tatters. Without the rockets the Russians will not defeat the British. There's just one thing I don't understand though," you tell the Inspector. "At the Exhibition I could smell your terrible cologne on Sir Archibald."

"Terrible cologne? I think you'll find we shared the same good taste!" the Inspector said with a chuckle. "Which reminds me, I've been asked to give you this, from Her Majesty the Queen," the Inspector reaches into his pocket, pulls out a leather case and hands it over.

"Of course, you can never tell anyone about what has happened…" he adds.

You open up the case. A bright gold medal glitters inside.

"You helped save the Empire from our enemies. You are a hero!"

Pirate Gold

Steve Barlow and Steve Skidmore

Illustrated by Sonia Leong

You are an English adventurer in the reign of Queen Elizabeth I.

Ever since Elizabeth became Queen, King Philip II of Spain has been looking for an excuse to invade England. Elizabeth and her navy are too weak to challenge Spain directly; so the Queen secretly employs 'gentleman pirates' to attack Spanish ships. The bravest and most successful of these is Francis Drake.

You set sail with Drake, and his brother John, with two ships, the *Pasha* and the *Swan*.

After several weeks crossing the Atlantic Ocean, you arrive on the Spanish Main (the Caribbean). Now you are about to strike your first blow against the Spanish with an attack on the harbour of Nombre de Dios.

I HERO
DECIDE YOUR OWN DESTINY
Pirate Gold
Steve Barlow - Steve Skidmore

All these I, Hero titles are available now!

978 0 7496 7664 3

978 0 7496 7665 0

978 0 7496 7666 7

978 0 7496 7667 4

978 0 7496 8265 1